HEAVEN SPENT©

Story & Illustrations
By Lara Toman

"Do not store up for yourselves treasures on Earth…
But store up for yourselves treasures in Heaven…"
~Matthew 6:19

There once was a boy
named Thomas who loved
to treasure hunt and collect
things.

One day when Thomas was playing outside, he found an old penny on the ground. He decided to save it.

He showed it to his dad, who said that if he saved enough of his pennies, he could buy whatever he wanted!

Thomas thought a lot about all the things that he could buy!

He began looking for pennies and saving them in a glass jar. He liked hunting for them, but some days he did not find any.

He began to count and learn about cost of things.

One day Thomas found a newer penny. He saw that people were tossing pennies into a fountain nearby.

Someone said, "make a wish at the fountain and throw it in, so your wish will come true!" So he did.

He made a wish and decided to let this one go instead of saving it.

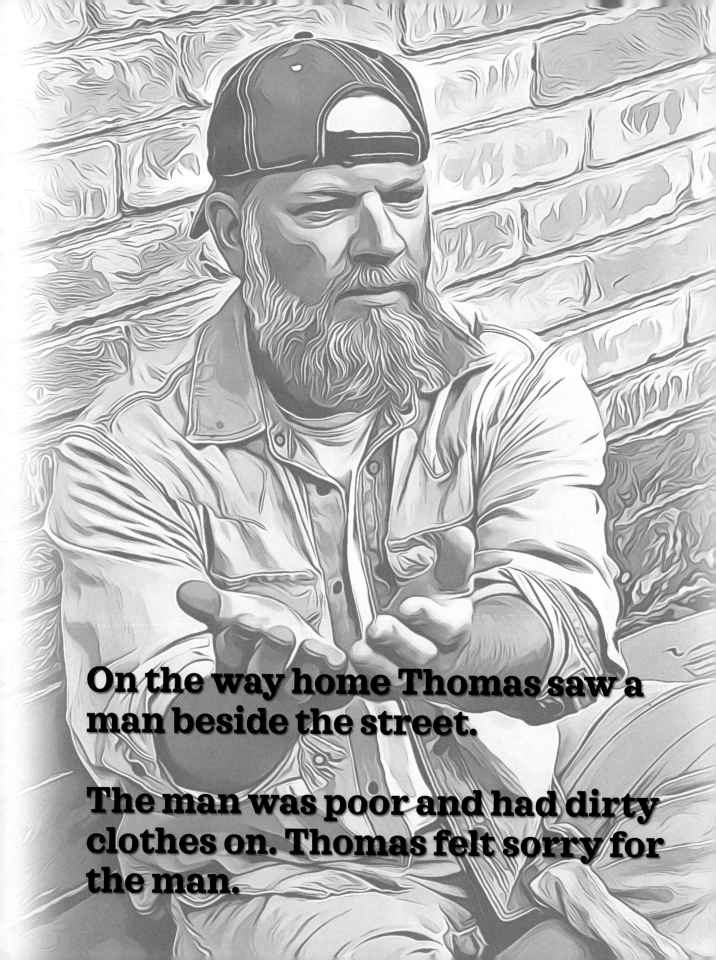

On the way home Thomas saw a man beside the street.

The man was poor and had dirty clothes on. Thomas felt sorry for the man.

He saw the man was holding a cup in his hands. he was counting his pennies and change from the cup.

He also noticed the man had no shoes on his feet.

That night Thomas had a dream about the poor man.

The next day he asked his mom if he could go back to the fountain.

His mother asked, "do you want to make another wish?"

"No" he said "but I need to get my penny back!"

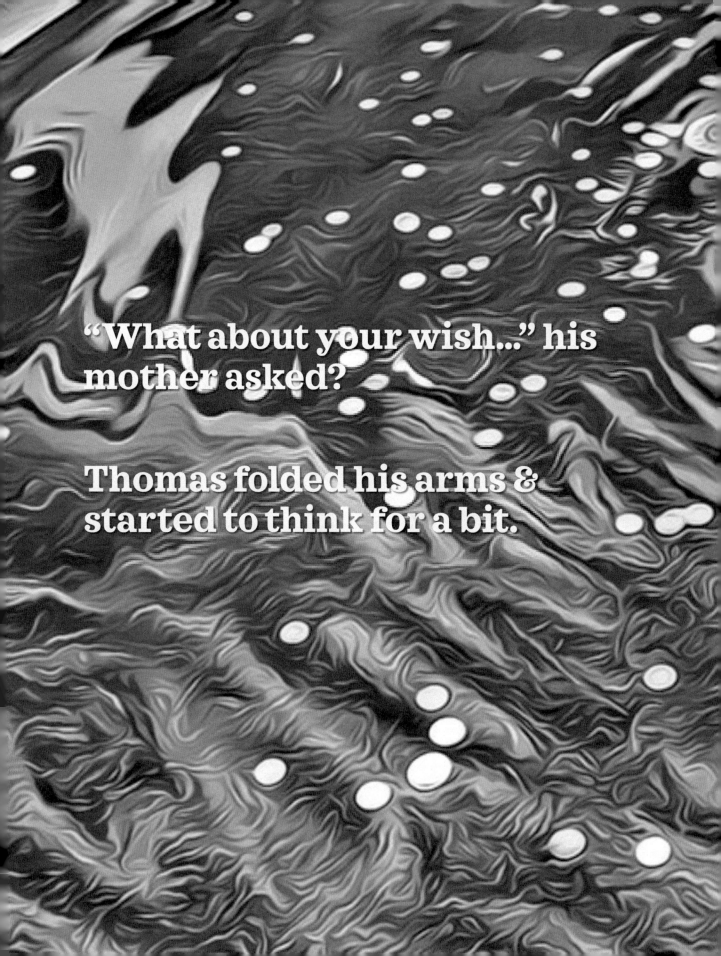

"What about your wish..." his mother asked?

Thomas folded his arms & started to think for a bit.

He saw lots of pennies in the fountain, but he did not know which one was his.

He also decided he did not want to get wet to get it back after all.

What to do??

He looked up at his mother, "Can I just change my wish," he asked? "Sure I think that's okay...it's *your* wish, so why not?" She smiled.

Thomas no longer wanted the toys he had been thinking about. He wanted the poor man to have shoes instead.

But he knew that to buy some would take so many pennies and lots of time.

So Thomas asked, "How do I change my wish?" His mother explained that if he closed his eyes and asked God, that she was sure that God would help, and the wish was surely to be fixed!

Thomas was happy to hear that, so they went home.

The next day Thomas came in from playing outside in the backyard. His mother was quietly praying at the table.

She was holding a string of beads with a cross on the end. When she finished Thomas asked, "What is that?"

Mom answered. "This?"
Thomas nodded. "This is
mommy's rosary" she said.

"What does it do?" He asked.

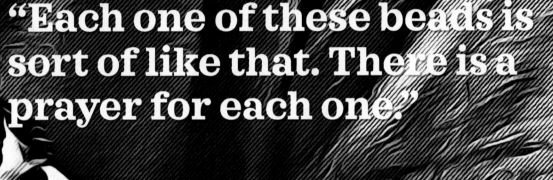

"Well" she answered, "Remember when we were at the fountain yesterday and you made your wish" She asked? He nodded.

"Each one of these beads is sort of like that. There is a prayer for each one."

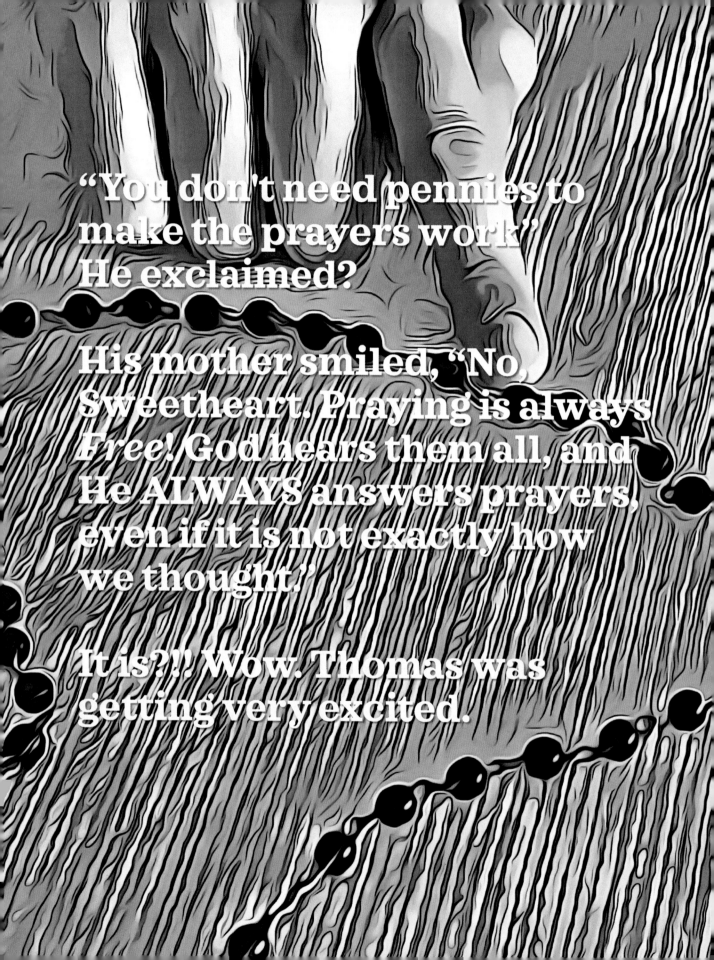

"You don't need pennies to make the prayers work" He exclaimed?

His mother smiled, "No, Sweetheart. Praying is always *Free!* God hears them all, and He ALWAYS answers prayers, even if it is not exactly how we thought."

It is?!' Wow. Thomas was getting very excited.

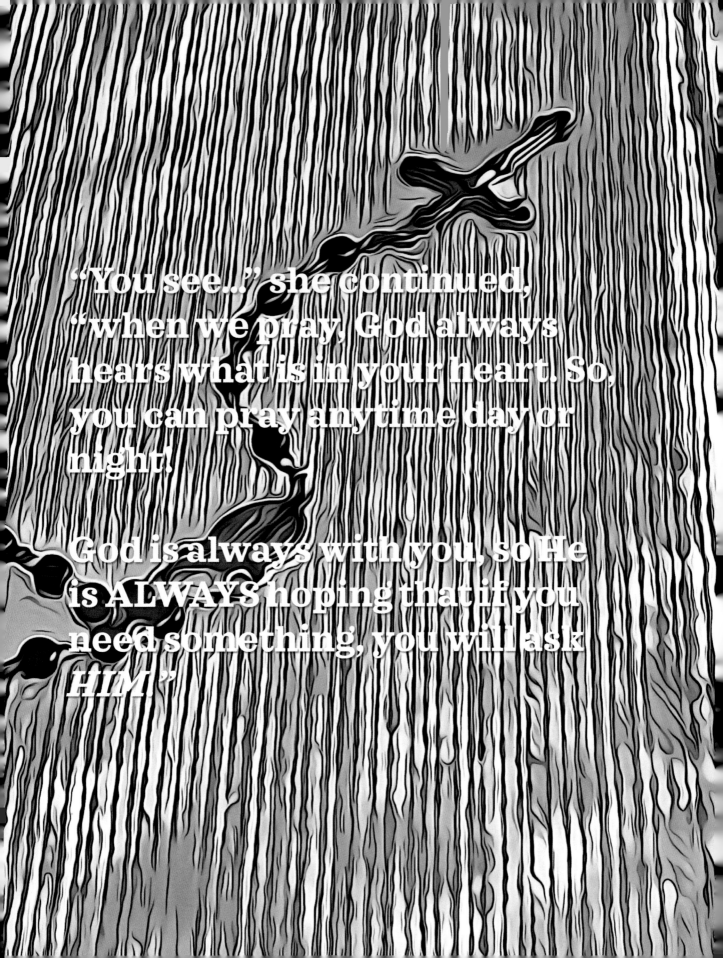

"You see..." she continued, "when we pray, God always hears what is in your heart. So, you can pray anytime day or night!

God is always with you, so He is ALWAYS hoping that if you need something, you will ask *HIM*."

"But Can I still make wishes if I find a penny?" He asked. "Of course!" She grinned.

 Thomas decided that he must now spend his wishes wisely! He remembered his mom's words about how God always wants us to think of Him, and ask God for everything.

As days passed Thomas would find a penny here or there.

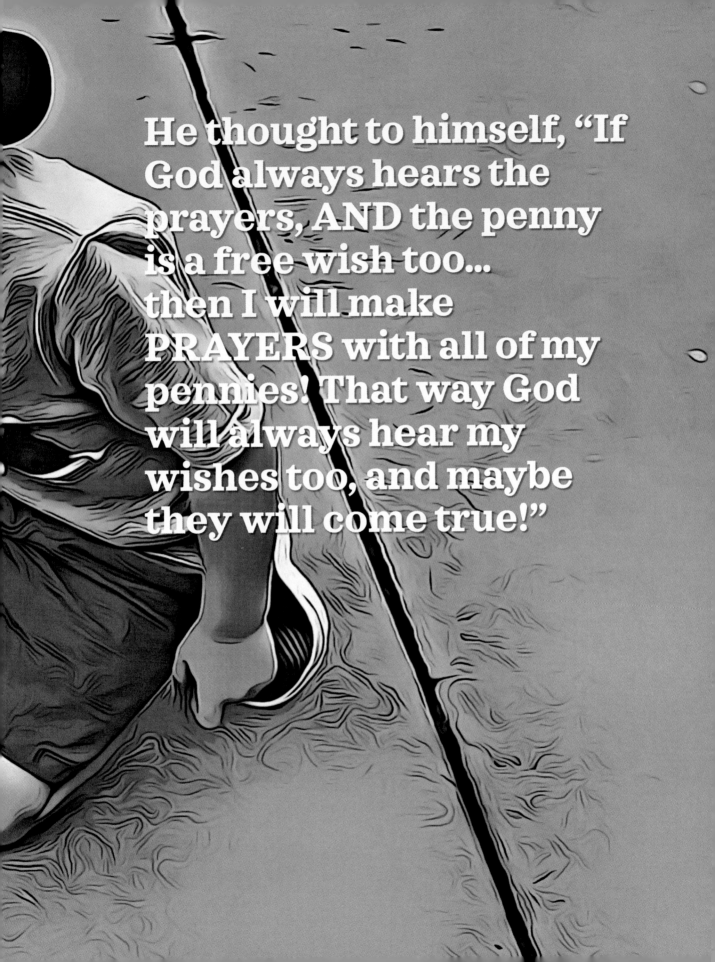

He thought to himself, "If God always hears the prayers, AND the penny is a free wish too... then I will make PRAYERS with all of my pennies! That way God will always hear my wishes too, and maybe they will come true!"

One day soon Thomas looked down he saw a copper flash on the ground "a penny!"

He quickly picked it up. He noticed the small letters on the top that read, "In God We Trust."

Looking at it he smiled. He looked up at the sky & felt in his heart the Lord Jesus, smiling back. He knew this penny was truly from Heaven!!

Then something amazing happened. Thomas heard a most beautiful loving voice from his heart. It was Jesus. "What will you ask for?" The Lord asked Thomas.

"Jesus, I want all my wishes to be the same. For every penny my every wish is ALWAYS to be closer to you!"

From that day on, Thomas found lots of pennies.

Each time he did he would put in his pocket and make his wish for the same prayer, "I want to be closer to God."

If he ever found a nickel or dime...even better! He simply counted that as 5 wishes, or 10 wishes to be even closer to God!

As time went on, Thomas had been saving them all in his jar. He knew he did not need the money for the prayers to come true, but seeing them all, his heart was happy that prayers were attached to all these wishes.

God was listening too!

That night when Thomas went to bed, he said his evening prayers and thanked God, then he climbed into bed.

As he slept, he dreamed he saw the poor man from before. He even remembered all the pennies in his dream!

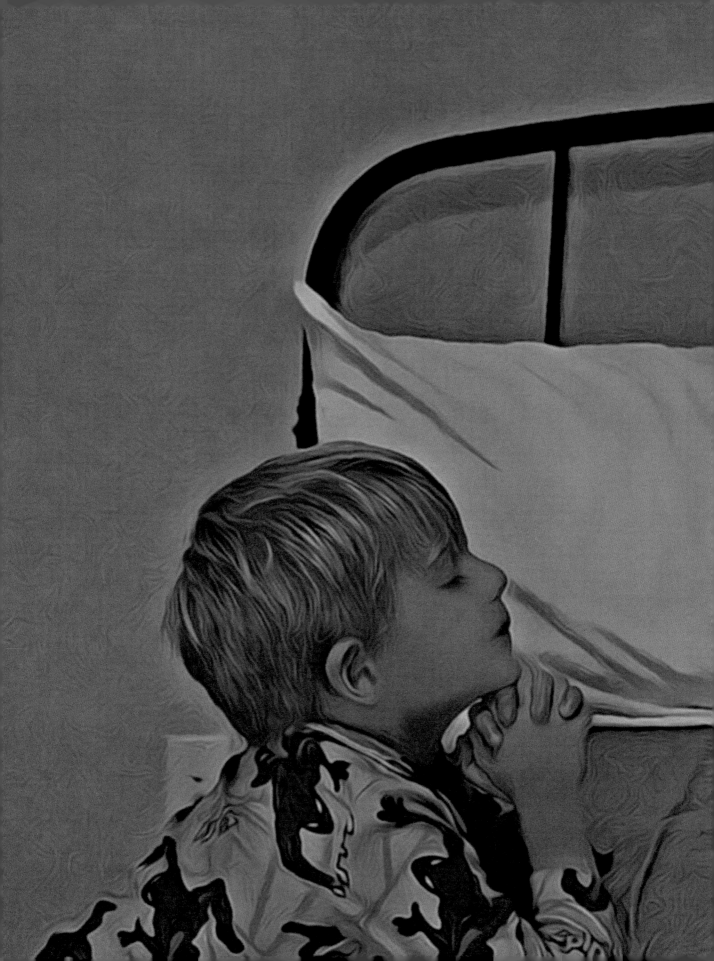

The next day Thomas took all the change he had, and asked his Dad to help him.

He counted enough to buy a pair of shoes!

Thomas needed help finding the poor man with no shoes so, they went out looking for the man. There he was on a different corner!

"There he is!!"

Thomas was a little scared to walk up to him. But he decided to be brave, and his Dad made him feel safe.

The man lifted his chin, and Thomas could see that he was blind. Thomas told him that he had brought him the shoes and some food.

When the man looked up, he had tears of joy in his eyes. Thomas smiled and helped him with the shoes, while Dad stood nearby.

"Thank you, thank you! My name is Sam" the man answered. "God bless you!"

That night Thomas told his mother about it all. When he fell asleep, he had a beautiful dream.

In the dream there was a large fountain like the one where he first prayed for Sam, but better! This place was so beautiful!!

Thomas heart heard music coming from the water and when he looked down, he saw no pennies inside. But he looked at his reflection and he saw the Lord beside him!

Thomas quickly looked up, and Jesus standing was with him. "Lord Jesus" He exclaimed!

Jesus grinned at him and said, "Thank you Thomas, for the shoes and food yesterday."

Thomas gasped. He realized that the man all along had been Jesus there!

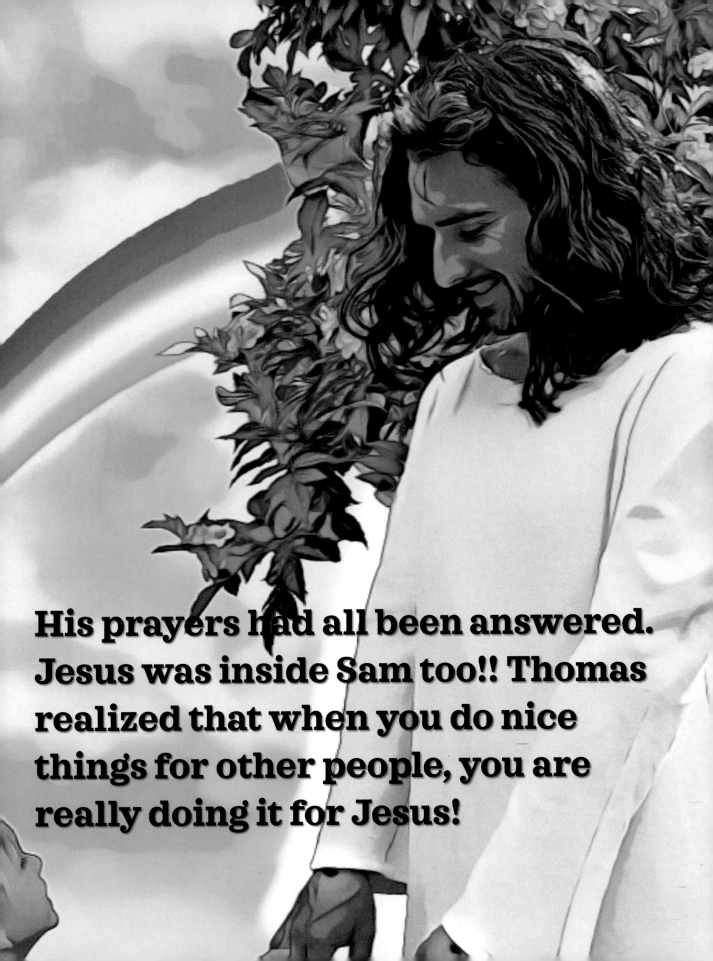

His prayers had all been answered. Jesus was inside Sam too!! Thomas realized that when you do nice things for other people, you are really doing it for Jesus!

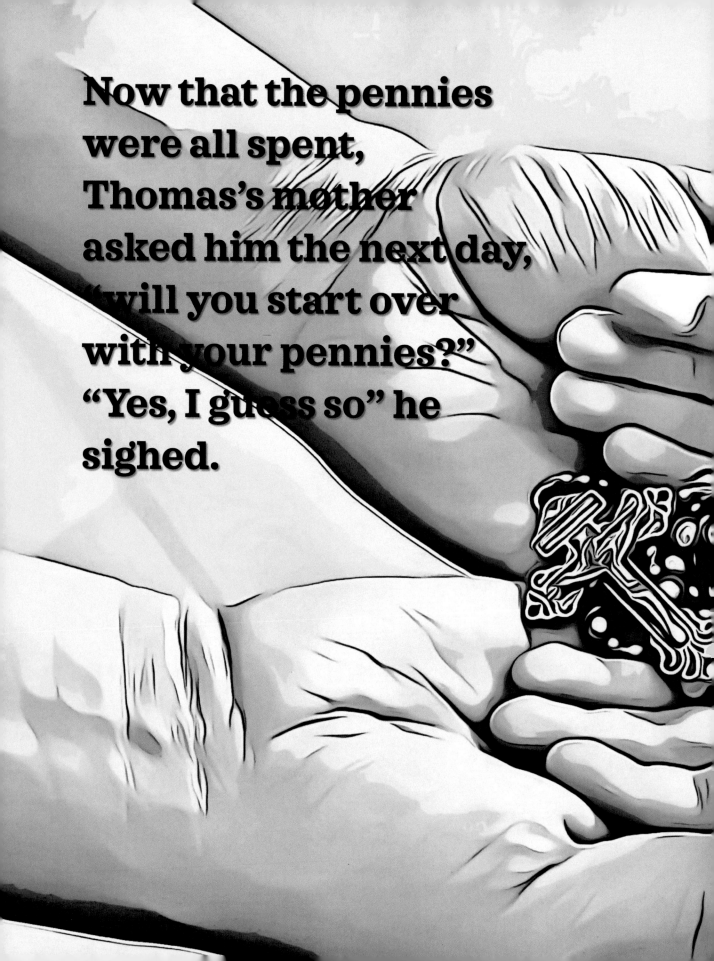

Now that the pennies were all spent, Thomas's mother asked him the next day, "will you start over with your pennies?" "Yes, I guess so" he sighed.

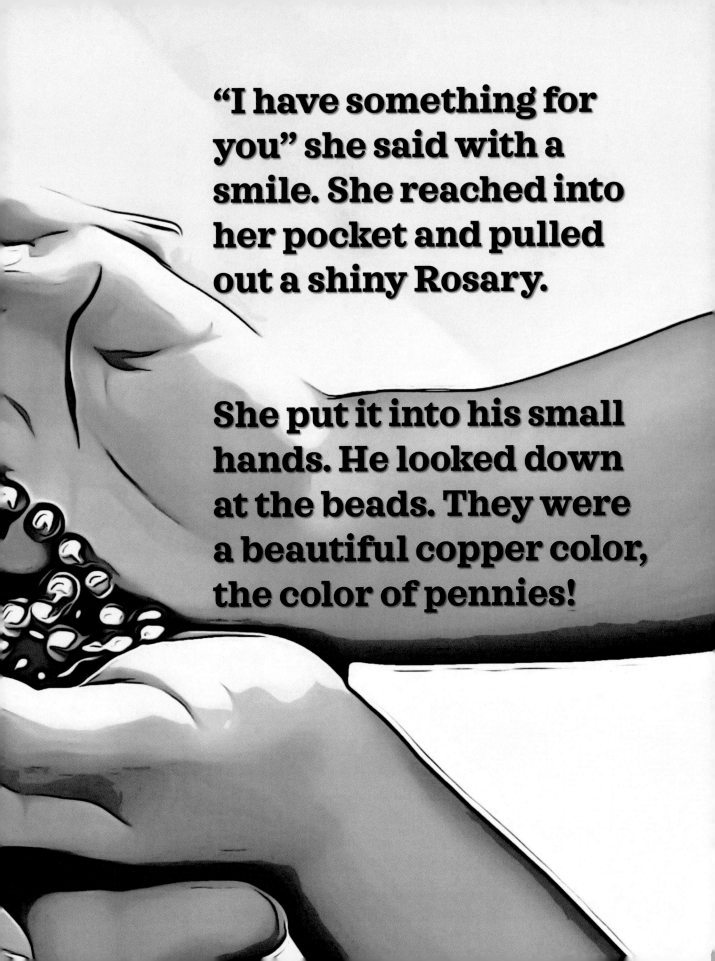

"I have something for you" she said with a smile. She reached into her pocket and pulled out a shiny Rosary.

She put it into his small hands. He looked down at the beads. They were a beautiful copper color, the color of pennies!

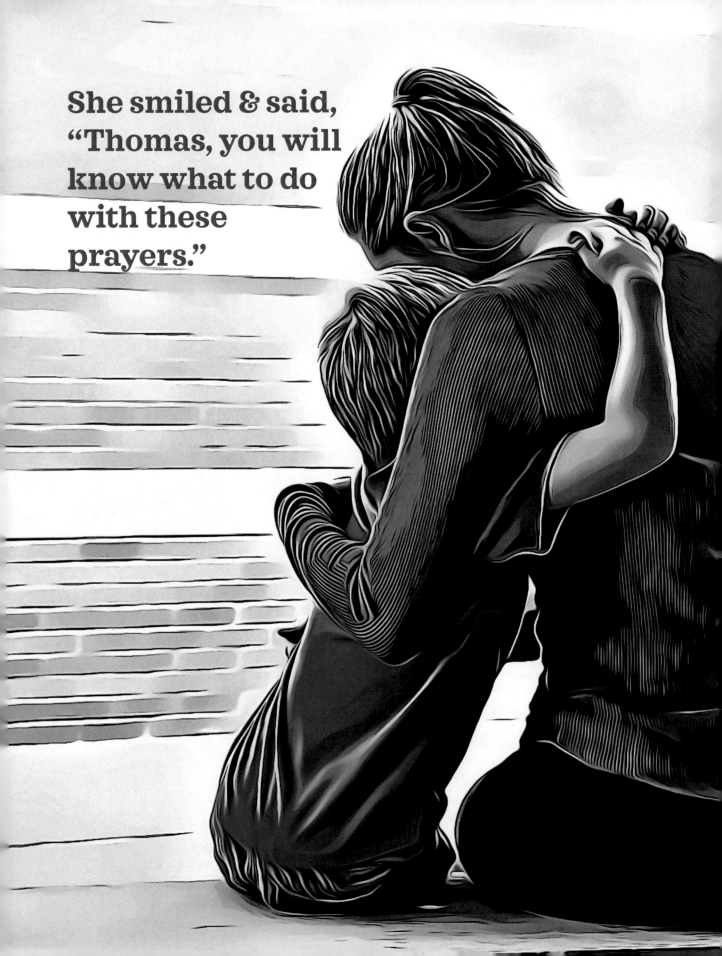

Thomas saved the Rosary and he kept it by his bed. Whenever he could not sleep, he would do his prayers in the dark. Sometimes he would wake up in the morning with it in his hands.

He remembered his time with Jesus and liked to pray his rosary by the fountain too. Thomas would sometimes sit and watch all the people making their wishes by the fountain.

Each time he saw this he made a special prayer in his heart.

Can you guess what his prayer was?

Thomas's prayer was....

"For all of *you* to be closer to God."

The End

All Glory, Honor & Praise to The
Father, The Son, & The Holy Spirit

Special Thanks to Hayes Acord,
Candace & Blaze Acord, Paul Davis
Andrew, Sofia, & T. Joseph Ozenne

Story & Illustrations Created
By Author, Lara Toman

✝

HEAVEN SPENT

Made in the USA
Coppell, TX
16 March 2021